Developing Nu[meracy]

HANDLING DATA

ACTIVITIES FOR THE DAILY MATHS LESSON

year
6

Hilary Koll and Steve Mills

A & C BLACK

Contents

Published 2002 by A & C Black Publishers Limited
37 Soho Square, London W1D 3QZ
www.acblack.com

ISBN 0-7136-6300-6

Copyright text © Hilary Koll and Steve Mills, 2002
Copyright illustrations © Gaynor Berry, 2002
Copyright cover illustration © Charlotte Hard, 2002
Editors: Lynne Williamson and Marie Lister

The authors and publishers would like to thank Jane McNeill and Corinne McCrum for their advice in producing this series of books.

A CIP catalogue record for this book is available from the British Library.

Printed in Great Britain by St Edmundsbury Press Ltd, Bury St Edmunds, Suffolk.

A & C Black uses paper produced with elemental chlorine-free pulp, harvested from managed sustainable forests.

Introduction

Developing Numeracy: Handling Data is a series of four photocopiable activity books for Key Stage 2, designed to be used during the daily maths lesson. It focuses on the fifth strand of the National Numeracy Strategy *Framework for teaching mathematics*. The activities are intended to be used in the time allocated to pupil activities; they aim to reinforce the knowledge and develop the facts, skills and understanding explored during the main part of the lesson. They provide practice and consolidation of the objectives contained in the framework document.

Year 6 supports the teaching of mathematics by providing a series of activities which develop essential skills in collecting, representing and interpreting numerical data. On the whole the activities are designed for children to work on independently, although this is not always possible and occasionally some children may need support.

Year 6 encourages children to:
- use the language associated with probability to discuss events, including those with equally likely outcomes. Discuss the chance or likelihood of particular events;
- solve a problem by collecting, organising, representing, extracting and interpreting data in tables, graphs, charts and diagrams, including those generated by a computer, for example
  - line graphs where intermediate points have meaning, including conversion graphs
  - frequency tables and bar charts with grouped discrete data
  - simple pie charts;
- make a simple database, and test hypotheses by interrogating data in a prepared computer database;
- find the mode and range of a set of data;
- begin to find the median and mean of a set of data.

Extension

Many of the activity sheets end with a challenge (**Now try this!**) which reinforces and extends the children's learning, and provides the teacher with the opportunity for assessment. The instructions are clearly presented so that children can work independently. On occasion, you may wish to read out the instructions and explain the activity before children begin working on it. For some of the challenges, the children will need to record their answers on a separate piece of paper. Sometimes the activity will require children to represent data in the form of a graph or chart and squared paper (or alternatively a computer with a handling data package) may be necessary.

Differentiated activities

Some of the activity sheets within this book are differentiated. A less challenging activity is indicated by a rocket icon: and a more challenging activity is indicated by a shooting star icon: . These activity sheets could be given to different groups within the class, or all children could complete the first sheet and children requiring further extension could then be given the second sheet.

Organisation

Very little equipment is needed, but it will be useful to have available: rulers, sharp pencils, squared paper, scissors, coloured pencils, counters, dice and ICT handling data software packages. You will need to provide coins for page 8, drawing pins for page 12, a video recording of a tennis match for page 21, football results for page 23, and a recipe in ounces for page 31. Blank probability scales, pie charts, bar chart and bar line chart/line graph are available on pages 43 to 46.

The activities in this book could be incorporated into lessons for other curriculum subjects, for example history, ICT, geography or science. The National Numeracy Strategy recommends exploiting opportunities for drawing on mathematical experience within other primary subjects, and handling data is a topic rich in cross-curricula investigations.

To help teachers select appropriate learning experiences for the children, the activities are grouped into sections within this book. However, the activities do not have to be used in that order unless otherwise stated. The sheets are intended to support, rather than direct, the teacher's planning.

Some activities can be made easier or more challenging by masking or substituting some of the numbers. You may wish to reuse some pages by copying them onto card and laminating them, or by enlarging them onto A3 paper.

ICT

On most occasions where pupils are asked to represent data in a graphical or tabular form, a computer could be used for this purpose. Some programs allow more than one type of graph to be drawn, and comparisons of this type are very useful. Spreadsheets could be used to assist children in collecting information as part of a survey.

Where children are researching their own topics for handling data, safe Internet sites could be used. Acceptable sites can often be accessed through a local educational authority's website or through kid-safe searches as part of most search engines. Some websites are suggested on page 5 and in the teacher's notes on the activity sheets.

Teachers' notes

Brief notes are provided at the foot of each page giving ideas and suggestions for maximising the effectiveness of the activity sheets. These can be masked before copying.

Whole-class warm-up activities

The following activities provide some practical ideas which can be used to introduce or reinforce the main teaching part of the lesson, or to provide an interesting basis for discussion.

Probability

Probability scale

Draw a probability scale split into sixths. Ask the children to draw arrows to show dice probabilities: for example, when using a 1 to 6 dice, the probability of rolling a 6, an odd number, a number less than 5, a multiple of 3, a multiple of 7 or a number below 10.

The chances are

Display the list below, and explain that these are accident figures for a stretch of road during one year.

Car accidents	102
Motorbike accidents	99
Lorry accidents	51
Van accidents	34
Bicycle accidents	1
Bus accidents	0
Total	**287**

Ask the children to discuss whether the following statements are true or false, or whether more information is required.

- *On this road:*
  - *a motorbike accident is more likely than a bus accident;*
  - *a van accident is more likely than a lorry accident;*
  - *a bicycle accident is unlikely;*
  - *a bus accident never happens;*
  - *a car accident is more likely than a bus accident.*
- *If you are travelling on this road, you are more likely to have an accident if you are in a car than if you are in any other vehicle.*
- *Because there might be more cars than buses, you would expect more car accidents than bus accidents.*
- *On any road, bus accidents are unlikely.*
- *On any road, motorbike accidents are more likely than lorry accidents.*

Pie charts

Circle proportions

Cut out two large circles of card, both the same size but each a different colour. Cut along the radius of each circle. Intersect the circles so that you can rotate one of them to show a proportion of the circle in a different colour. Turn it to show a sector (such as 180°, 90°, 45° or 120°). Ask the children to say what proportion of the whole is shown (for example, one half or one quarter). Ask: *If the whole circle represents 24 people, how many people does this sector represent?*

Mean, median and mode

Scores

Ask the children to call out some two-digit numbers, and write them randomly in two columns on the board, one column labelled 'A' and the other 'B'. Explain that these are scores. Split the class into two teams (team A and team B). Ask children from each team to find the mode (or modal values), median and mean for their set of scores. The children will require a calculator for this. Award a point for each average to the team that has the higher number.

Easily accessible sources and further ideas

The following suggestions for real-life data can be used as a stimulus for further data work.

Newspapers These contain a wealth of information, for example: TV programme listings, football tables, sports results, temperature readings and weather reports. They can also be analysed with questions such as *How many letter As are in this report?*

Travel brochures Children can investigate temperatures, compare prices, find out which destinations have most hotels with swimming pools, and so on.

Magazines Look out for survey results presented in charts or graphs for the children to interpret, as well as questionnaires that the children can answer themselves.

The school and children themselves Investigate measures of objects in school, different ball diameters, growth of houseplants/seedlings, children's standing jump results, cooking and food technology activities, activities children undertake at home/during holidays, and so on.

Calendars Children can analyse the information on calendars. Ask questions such as: *What day is the first/last/sixth of each month? In which month do most children in the class have a birthday?*

Useful websites

www.standards.dfes.gov.uk/numeracy
www.dinosaurworld.com/facts.html
www.metoffice.gov.uk/education/data
www.schoolhistory.co.uk
www.georesources.co.uk

Alien zap!

- **Colour each alien on the path a different colour. In this game, you roll two dice, find the total and move forward that many squares. If you land on an alien, you 'zap' it. Then return to start.**

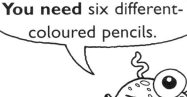
You need six different-coloured pencils.

- **Answer questions 1 and 2 <u>before</u> you play.**

1. Which colour alien do you think you are **most likely** to zap? _____

2. Is there an alien you think it is **impossible** to zap? If so, which one? _____

| start | | | | | |

3. Now play the game. Roll two dice and find the total. Mark the square you land on with a tally, then return to start. Do this 50 times.

You need two dice and a counter.

4. Were your predictions correct? Explain your answer on the back of this sheet.

Now try this!

- **Write all the possible totals you can get when rolling two dice.**

Example:
1 + 1 = 2
1 + 2 = 3   2 + 1 = 3
1 + 3 = 4   2 + 2 = 4   3 + 1 = 4
                                        and so on

Teachers' note This activity could be done in pairs. Remind the children that the more times an experiment is done, the more likely the results are to reflect the mathematical probability gained through listing possibilities. Here there are 36 possibilities, six of which have the total 7, whereas only one has the total 2 (or 12). Each *possibility* is an equally likely outcome, however each *total* is not.

Developing Numeracy Handling Data Year 6
© A & C Black 2002

A tenths moment

• **Colour all the sweets in the bags so that the probability statements are true.**

You need red, yellow, blue and green coloured pencils.

1. The probability of picking

   a **red** sweet is 1 out of 10 or $\frac{1}{10}$, and

   a **blue** sweet is 3 out of 10 or $\frac{3}{10}$.

2. The probability of picking

   a **yellow** sweet is 5 out of 10 or $\frac{5}{10}$, and

   a **green** sweet is 2 out of 10 or $\frac{2}{10}$.

3. The probability of picking

   a **red** sweet is $\frac{4}{10}$, a **blue** sweet is $\frac{1}{10}$,

   and a **yellow** sweet is $\frac{3}{10}$.

4. The probability of picking a **yellow**

   sweet is $\frac{7}{10}$. There is an equal probability of

   picking a **red, blue** or **green** sweet.

5. The probability of picking a **green**

   sweet is $\frac{4}{10}$. There is an equal probability of

   picking a **red, blue** or **yellow** sweet.

Now try this!

• **Draw four bags of your own. Draw eight sweets in each. Colour the sweets.**
• **Write three probability statements for each bag.**

Teachers' note The children could plot these probabilities on a number line split into tenths. Ask questions such as: *Which coloured sweet is most likely to be picked? Which has the lowest probability?* As a further extension, ask: *If all the sweets on the page are put into a bag and one is picked, which colour is it most likely to be?*

**Developing Numeracy
Handling Data Year 6
© A & C Black 2002**

Heads or tails?

When you toss a coin, it comes up heads or tails .

You need a coin.

1. What is the probability of the coin coming up heads? _____

2. About how many times would it come up heads if you tossed it:

(a) twice? _____ (b) 20 times? _____ (c) 80 times? _____

• **Toss a coin 20 times. Record your results on the snake. Write H or T in each box.**

3. How many times did the coin come up heads? _____

4. If you repeat this experiment, do you think you will get the same

number of heads? _____

Why? _____

_____

• **Now repeat the experiment. Write your results here:**

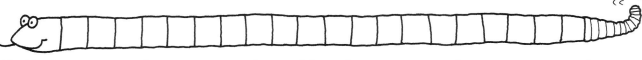

5. Did you toss the same number of heads as in your first experiment? _____

6. From the **40 times** you tossed the coin, how many times in total did

it come up heads? _____

• **Now join up with a partner.**

7. How many heads did your partner toss in their 40 throws? _____

8. Is this about the same number as you tossed? _____

9. From the 80 times you and your partner tossed a coin, how many

times did the coin come up heads? _____

• **Add your results to the results of nine other pairs.**
What do you notice? _____

_____

Teachers' note Ask the children whether their findings were close to what they expected. Encourage them to discuss and become aware of the difference between the theory of outcomes (one chance out of two $= \frac{1}{2}$), and the actual results. During the plenary, discuss that the greater number of times an event is explored in this way, the closer it is likely to be to the theoretical probability.

**Developing Numeracy
Handling Data Year 6
© A & C Black 2002**

Famous people cards: 1

Cards showing famous people come free with boxes of cereal. Jo has collected these 10 cards.

 Isaac Newton    Isaac Newton    Marie Curie    Alexander Graham Bell    Robert Louis Stevenson

 Florence Nightingale    Isaac Newton    Marie Curie    Isaac Newton    Albert Einstein

- **If Jo picks one of her cards without looking, what is the probability of her picking:**

1. Florence Nightingale? $\frac{1}{10}$ **2.** Marie Curie? _____

3. Albert Einstein? _____   **4.** Isaac Newton? _____

5. Robert Louis Stevenson? _____   **6.** Michael Faraday? _____

7. a woman? _____   **8.** a man? _____

9. a person with the letter **a** in their name? _____

10. a person with the letter **i** in their name? _____

11. a person with the letter **o** in their name? _____

12. a person with the letter **u** in their name? _____

13. a person with the letter **e** in their name? _____

 Now try this!

- **Jo adds these cards to her collection. What is the probability of her picking a person with three words in their name?** _____

 Vincent Van Gogh    William Shakespeare

Give the fraction in its **simplest** form.

Teachers' note Before beginning, ensure the children appreciate that probabilities can be expressed as fractions where the denominator indicates the number of possibilities, for example 4 cards out of 10 show Newton, so the probability of picking him is 4 out of 10. This can be written as $\frac{4}{10}$. Ask the children to give answers as fractions and, if appropriate, to write them in their simplest form.

**Developing Numeracy
Handling Data Year 6
© A & C Black 2002**

Fatima has collected these 8 cards showing famous people.

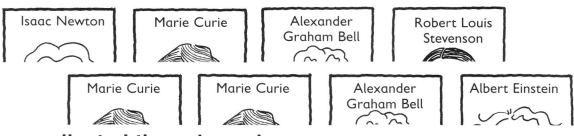

Isaac Newton

Marie Curie

Alexander Graham Bell

Robert Louis Stevenson

Marie Curie

Marie Curie

Alexander Graham Bell

Albert Einstein

Jack has collected these 4 cards.

Marie Curie

Marie Curie

Alexander Graham Bell

Robert Louis Stevenson

Both Fatima and Jack pick one of their cards without looking.

- **Mark the scales with arrows to show the probability of each child picking:**

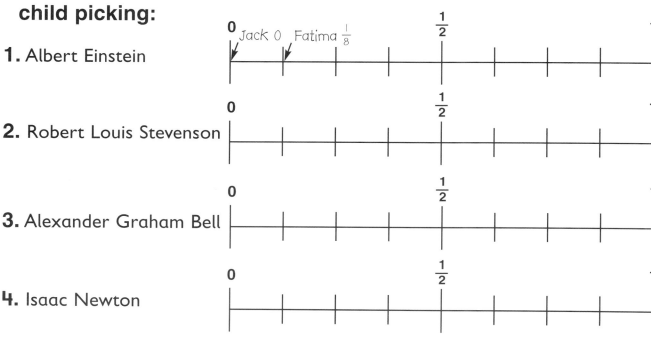

1. Albert Einstein

0   Jack 0   Fatima $\frac{1}{8}$ $\frac{1}{2}$ 1

2. Robert Louis Stevenson

0   $\frac{1}{2}$ 1

3. Alexander Graham Bell

0   $\frac{1}{2}$ 1

4. Isaac Newton

0   $\frac{1}{2}$ 1

5. Marie Curie

0   $\frac{1}{2}$ 1

Now try this!

- **Draw a set of 10 cards. Make the probability of picking a woman equal $\frac{6}{10}$. Make the probability of picking a living person equal $\frac{7}{10}$.**

Teachers' note Ensure the children appreciate that these probabilities can be expressed as fractions where the denominator indicates the number of cards altogether, and the numerator indicates the number of cards with a particular feature. Revision of equivalent fractions may be necessary. By using a line, the children can appreciate that most probabilities on this sheet are 'unlikely'.

**Developing Numeracy
Handling Data Year 6
© A & C Black 2002**

Chance in a million?

Your teacher will give you a sheet of probability scales.

☆ Cut out the cards. Mix them up and spread them face down.

☆ Pick three cards. Put them in order of likelihood.

☆ Mark the three probabilities on one of the scales.

☆ Pick another three cards and do the same on another scale. Continue until all the cards are used up.

a When you roll a 1 to 6 dice you will get a **multiple of 3**.	**b** When you roll a 1 to 6 dice you will get a **multiple of 2**.
c When you roll a 1 to 6 dice you will get a **6**.	**d** When you roll a 1 to 6 dice you will get an **odd** number.
e When you roll a 1 to 6 dice you will get a number **less than 3**.	**f** When you roll a 1 to 6 dice you will get a number **greater than 4**.
g When you roll a 1 to 6 dice you will get a number **between 0 and 7**.	**h** When you roll a 1 to 6 dice you will get a number **greater than 2**.
i When you roll a 1 to 6 dice you will get a **4**.	**j** When you roll a 1 to 6 dice you will get a number **less than 6**.
k You will get a **0** when you pick from a set of 0 to 5 digit cards.	**l** You will get an **even** number when you pick from a set of 0 to 5 digit cards.
m You will get an **odd** number when you pick from a set of 0 to 5 digit cards.	**n** You will get a number **less than 5** when you pick from a set of 0 to 5 digit cards.
o You will get a number **less than 3** when you pick from a set of 0 to 5 digit cards.	**p** You will get a **1** when you pick from a set of 0 to 5 digit cards.
q You will get a **multiple of 3** when you pick from a set of 0 to 5 digit cards.	**r** You will get a number **greater than 3** when you pick from a set of 0 to 5 digit cards.

Teachers' note The children could work in pairs. They will need a copy of the blank probability scales on page 43. Some children may need each line splitting into sixths. If necessary, provide a dice and a set of 0 to 5 digit cards. Point out that there are six cards, marked 0 to 5. As an extension, the children could write two cards of their own, one where the probability is **0** and one where the probability is **1**.

**Developing Numeracy
Handling Data Year 6
© A & C Black 2002**

Equally likely

- **Tick the probability situations that have two** equally likely **outcomes.**

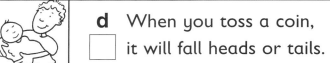

a When you drop a postcard, ☐ it will land picture side up or picture side down.	**b** When you roll a 1 to 6 ☐ dice, the number will be odd or even.
c A new baby will be ☐ a boy or a girl.	**d** When you toss a coin, ☐ it will fall heads or tails.
e When you pick a card ☐ from a set of playing cards, it will be a picture card or a number card.	**f** When you pick a card ☐ from a set of playing cards, it will be a red card or a black card. 
g When you pick a day of ☐ the week at random, it will contain a **t** or will not contain a **t**. 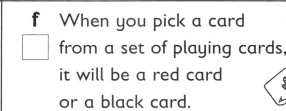	**h** When you pick a month ☐ of the year at random, it will contain an **a** or will not contain an **a**.

- **Read the situations below. For each one, make up a** fair test **to see whether the two outcomes might be equally likely. Repeat the test many times (30 or more). Record the results.**

> **You need** two 1 to 6 dice and a drawing pin.

When you roll two 1 to 6 dice, the total will be **above 7** or **below 8**.

When you drop a drawing pin, it will land **point up** or **point down**.

Now try this!

- **Write a report about your tests. Explain what your tests tell you about the probabilities.**

> Did each test show an equally likely outcome?

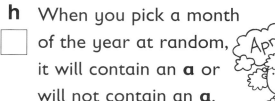

Teachers' note Discuss the terms 'equally likely', 'fair' and 'random' before the children start the activity. The children could work in pairs. Count the drawing pins as you give them out and collect them carefully afterwards. Encourage the children to use tallying to record results. Discuss that a theoretically equally likely outcome might not produce exactly the same results practically.

Developing Numeracy Handling Data Year 6 © A & C Black 2002

Database magic: 1

- **Work with a partner.**

☆ Cut out the cards, then cut carefully along the dotted lines.

☆ Put the cards in a pile with the **dog** card on the top. Make sure
all the cards are the right way up and facing the front. Hold the pile upright.

☆ Put a pencil through the hole marked **Does it fly?** Lift the pencil. *Which cards fall?*

☆ Put the cards in a pile again. Put a pencil through the hole marked **Is it a bird?**
Lift the pencil. *Which cards fall?*

☆ Put the cards in a pile again. Put pencils through both holes. *Which cards fall?*

- **Write a database like this to
show the information.**

Creature	Is it a bird?	Does it fly?
dog	no	no

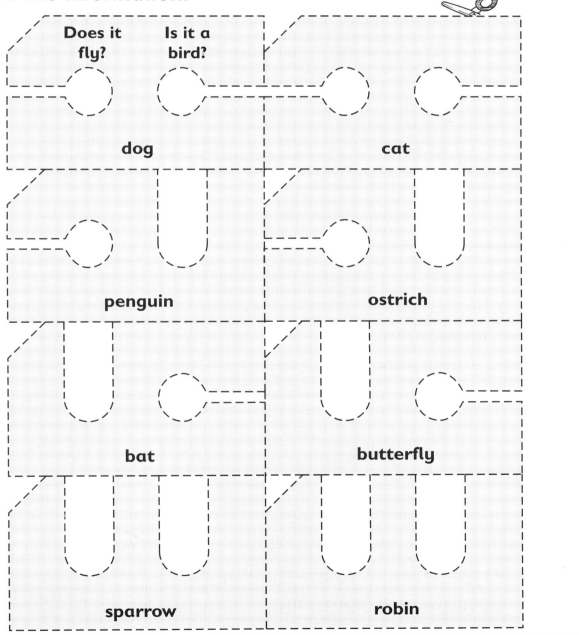

Developing Numeracy
Handling Data Year 6
© A & C Black 2002

Database magic: 2

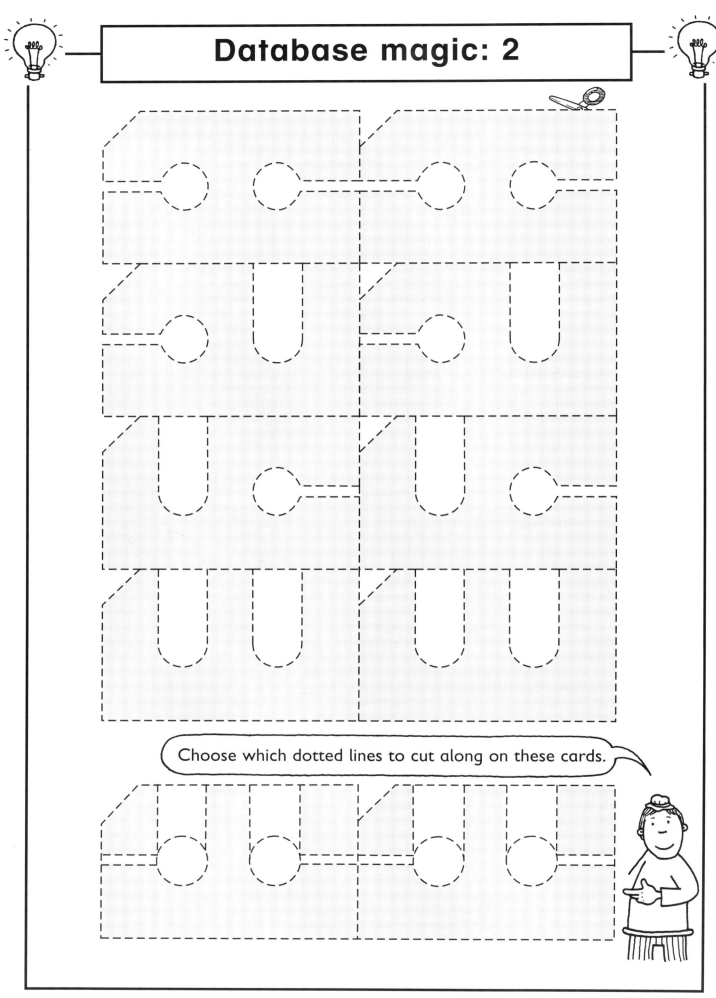

Choose which dotted lines to cut along on these cards.

Teachers' note This sheet provides database cards to use in the same way as those on page 13. Questions such as 'Does it have 4 legs?' and 'Is it a mammal?' can be asked for the following animals: horse, blackbird, lizard, dolphin, human, frog, rat and beetle. The children should cut along the *vertical* dotted lines if the answer is 'yes'. Ask the children to write a simple database like the one on page 13.

Developing Numeracy
Handling Data Year 6
© A & C Black 2002

Masses of birds

This database shows the approximate length **and** mass **of garden birds.**

Bird name	Approx. length (cm)	Approx. mass (g)
robin	14	17
blue tit	12	11
swallow	21	18
chiffchaff	11	8
wren	10	10
great tit	14	17
greenfinch	15	27
song thrush	23	70
blackbird	26	100
mistle thrush	27	99
dunnock	15	20
goldcrest	9	6
starling	21	69
treecreeper	12	9
chaffinch	15	30

Do you think that the longer a bird is, the heavier it is?

1. Which bird is:

(a) the longest? _____

(b) the shortest? _____

(c) the heaviest? _____

(d) the lightest? _____

2. What is the length of:

(a) a starling? _____   **(b)** a wren? _____

3. What is the mass of:

(a) a chiffchaff? _____   **(b)** a mistle thrush? _____

4. (a) Which birds have a length of 12 cm? _____

(b) What are their masses? _____

5. (a) Which birds have a length of 21 cm? _____

(b) What are their masses? _____

6. (a) Which birds have a mass of 17 g? _____

(b) What are their lengths? _____

Now try this!

• **Write two lists of the birds, first in order of length, then in order of mass. Start with the smallest.**

In order of length   *In order of mass*

Are longer birds always heavier?

Teachers' note Use gram weights to help the children appreciate how light these birds are. Explain that birds have hollow bones that are very light, allowing them to fly. The data could be keyed into a computer spreadsheet and the details explored on screen. Other features can be investigated, such as finding birds that are particularly light for their size (for example a swallow).

Developing Numeracy Handling Data Year 6 © A & C Black 2002

Bowling scores

• **Look at the database. It shows 20 people who visited a bowling alley. It gives each person's name, age and score.**

Name	Age	Score
Danny	7	37
Nagajan	11	45
Lesley	34	93
Vincento	45	99
Kylie	24	113
Edith	84	89
Deepa	18	95
Chandu	6	54
Alfred	66	87
Dorothy	54	117
Gordon	49	70
Rebecca	11	100
Mabel	94	67
Franco	38	73
Lauren	9	69
Jeremy	40	101
Jennie	36	87
Sam	24	70
David	8	42
Chloe	15	84

Do you think that the older people are, the better they are at bowling?

1. Who is the youngest? _____

2. Who is the oldest? _____

3. Who has the highest score? _____

4. Who has the lowest score? _____

5. Write the score of:

    (a) Deepa _____   **(b)** Franco _____

6. **(a)** Which people are 24 years old? _____

    (b) What are their scores? _____

7. **(a)** Which people scored 87? _____

    (b) How old are they? _____

8. What is the range of: **(a)** ages? _____ **(b)** scores? _____

9. Did most people under 20 score less than 80? _____

10. Did most people over 60 score more than 100? _____

Now try this!

• **Write two lists of the people:**

    (a) in order of age, youngest first

    (b) in order of scores, starting with the lowest.

| **In order of age** | **In order of scores** |

Are older people better at bowling?

Teachers' note Revise the term 'range' if necessary. The data could be keyed into a computer spreadsheet and the details explored on screen. Encourage children to investigate and describe any correlations that they can see between ages and scores, for example, that people between 10 and 20 years of age score more highly than those under the age of 10, and so on.

Developing Numeracy Handling Data Year 6 © A & C Black 2002

16

Card averages

- **Find these values for each set of playing cards.**

 The **ace** represents the number **1**.

1.(a) the range _____

  (b) the mode _____

  (c) the median _____

  (d) the mean _____

2.

  (a) the range _____

  (b) the mode _____

  (c) the median _____

  (d) the mean _____

3.(a) the range _____

  (b) the mode _____

  (c) the median _____

  (d) the mean _____

4.

  (a) the range _____

  (b) the mode _____

  (c) the median _____

  (d) the mean _____

5.(a) the range _____

  (b) the mode _____

  (c) the median _____

  (d) the mean _____

6.

  (a) the range _____

  (b) the mode _____

  (c) the median _____

  (d) the mean _____

   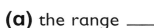  

 Now try this!

- **Pick ten digit cards.**
- **Find the** ⬚range⬚ , ⬚mode⬚ , ⬚median⬚ **and** ⬚mean⬚ .

Teachers' note Revise the terms range, mode, median and mean. This activity involves whole number means and can be solved without using a calculator. Remind children that there can be more than one mode or modal value, and that if there are two middle numbers the median is the number that lies between the two, for example between 6 and 7 the median is $6\frac{1}{2}$ or 6·5.

Developing Numeracy Handling Data Year 6 © A & C Black 2002

- **Look at the fish.**

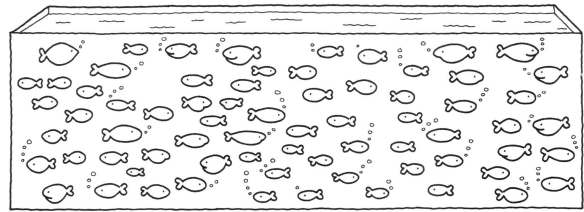

- **Without counting, estimate the number of fish.** _____
- **Find out the estimates of nine other people in your class. Make a list.**

List of estimates

- **Now answer these questions about your data.**

1. What is the **range** of the estimates? _____

2. What is the **mode** of the estimates? _____

3. What is the **median** of the estimates? _____

4. What is the **mean** of the estimates? _____

5. Was your estimate higher or lower than the mean? _____

Now try this!

- **Count the fish. Was the mode, median or mean closest to the <u>actual</u> number of fish?** _____

Teachers' note Read out the children's names in turn and ask them to call out their estimates. Each child should write down their own estimate and nine others. Data can be grouped to find the modal group where appropriate. Allow the children to use calculators to work out the mean, so that the focus of attention is on how it is found rather than on the calculation itself.

**Developing Numeracy
Handling Data Year 6
© A & C Black 2002**

Magic Meg

Meg the magician picks some 0 to 9 digit cards. She puts them on the table and turns some of them over.

- **Work out what the blank cards are.**

Some cards could have more than one answer.

1. The mode of these cards is 4.

| 2 | 4 | 3 | 7 | 4 |

2. The range of these cards is 6.

| 2 | 5 | 3 | 3 | |

3. The median of these cards is 4.

| 8 | 4 | 3 | 1 |

4. The mean of these cards is 4.

| 5 | 4 | 3 | 5 | |

5. The median of these cards is 5.

| 2 | 9 | 3 | 7 | |

6. The mean of these cards is 6.

| 8 | 0 | 8 | 7 | |

7. The median of these cards is 7·5.

| 2 | 8 | 3 | | | |

8. The range of these cards is 4 and the mean is 6.

| | | |

Five digit cards are the <u>same</u>.

- **The mean is 6. What is the:**

mode? _____   range? _____   median? _____

Teachers' note Remind the children of the meanings of the different averages. You could also ask them to find the range, mode, median and mean for each set of cards. This will involve means that are not whole numbers (the children could use calculators). Remind them that, if two numbers are in the middle, the median is the value half-way between them, for example 2, 7, 8, 9 has a median of 7·5.

Developing Numeracy
Handling Data Year 6
© A & C Black 2002

TV channels

• **Look at the bar chart. It shows the number of TV channels in the UK from 1927 to 1997.**

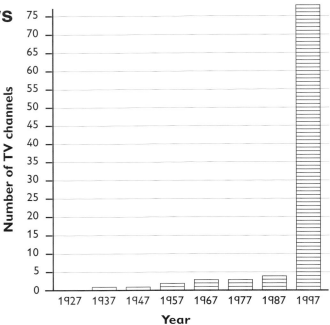

1. How many channels were there in:

(a) 1947? _____

(b) 1977? _____

(c) 1987? _____

(d) 1997? _____

2. What is the difference between the number of channels in:

(a) 1947 and 1957? _____   **(b)** 1967 and 1977? _____

(c) 1977 and 1987? _____   **(d)** 1987 and 1997? _____

> **The first channel to broadcast was BBC1. The second was ITV, the third BBC2 and the fourth Channel 4.**

3. Between which years did the following channels first broadcast?

(a) BBC2? _____   **(b)** ITV? _____

(c) Channel 4? _____   **(d)** BBC1? _____

4. What do you think happened between 1987 and 1997?

_____

5. Find the mode and the mean number(s) of channels for the years in the graph. Is this information useful? Why/why not? _____

_____

_____

• **How many TV channels do you think there will be in 2007? Explain your answer.** _____

_____

Teachers' note Invite the children to express their opinions of why the number of TV channels might have changed. Ensure the children realise that there can be more than one mode. This real data involves values with a large range thus the averages are less representative.

**Developing Numeracy
Handling Data Year 6
© A & C Black 2002**

Tennis tally

You are going to watch part of a tennis match on TV.

- **For each point, count how many times a racket hits the ball until the point is won. Record it on the tally chart.**

Hits per point	Tally	Frequency
1–2		
3–4		
5–6		
7–8		
9–10		
11–12		
13–14		
15–16		

1. (a) Which group/groups have the highest frequency? _____

(b) Why might this be? _____

_____

2. Which group/groups have the lowest frequency? _____

3. Do you think this will be the same for all tennis matches? Why?

_____

4. How many points did you watch in total? _____

- **Now draw a** bar chart **to show this information.**

Now try this!

- **If there are 200 points in the whole tennis match, about how many times might the ball be hit?** _____

Decide on the most suitable number of hits per point to use in your calculation.

Teachers' note Video part of a match and decide on a suitable number of points to show. Explain the scoring system and what a point is. A blank bar chart is available on page 45. The children could be shown parts of two matches with different players and compare the results. Discuss possible reasons for any differences, for example, players with stronger serves may hit the ball fewer times.

**Developing Numeracy
Handling Data Year 6
© A & C Black 2002**

How long is your name?

Do you think most people in your class have between 11 and 20 letters in their name?

Christopher Timothy Smythe

Do you think that boys' names have more letters than girls' names?

- **Count the number of letters in your full name. Include your first, middle and family names.**

Number of letters

- **As each person calls out the number of letters in his or her name, write the number in the correct grid below.**

Don't forget to include your own name!

Boys

Girls

- **Find the range of all the values.** _____

- **Draw a frequency table for either boys or girls. Group the data like this. Use tallying.**

Letters	Tally	Frequency
1–5		
6–10		
11–15		
16–20		
21–25		

1. Which group has the highest frequency (modal group)? _____

2. Make up two questions to ask about your table. Write them on the back of this sheet. **Example:** *How many girls have more than 20 letters in their name?*

- **Draw a bar chart to show the data in your frequency table.**

3. Consider whether most people in your class have between 11 and 20 letters in their name. Can the information above help you to answer this? _____ Why/why not? _____

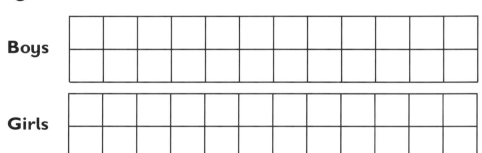

Now try this!

- **Write six statements about your bar chart.**

Teachers' note Read out the children's names in turn and ask them to call out the number of letters in their full name. A blank bar chart is available on page 45. Discuss the need for grouping data when there are many different values. Show how, if each number had a separate column on a bar chart, the chart would be too large! During the plenary, compile the results to test the hypotheses in the bubbles.

Developing Numeracy Handling Data Year 6 © A & C Black 2002

Your teacher will give you some football results which show the times when goals were scored.

The number after the player's name shows the minute in which the goal was scored.

Spurs 0   Leeds 2 (Fowler 43, Smith 67)

• Organise the data into groups on the chart.

Time (minutes)	Tally	Frequency
1–15		
16–30		
31–45		
46–60		
61–75		
76–90		

1. What is the range of times of goals scored? _____

2. How many goals were scored between 46 and 60 minutes? _____

3. Between which minutes were: **(a)** most goals scored? _____

    (b) fewest goals scored? _____

4. Were more goals scored before half time

    (up to 45 minutes) or after half time? _____

5. How many goals were scored in total? _____

Now try this!

• Draw a bar chart to show the information.

Teachers' note Provide copies of football results from a Sunday paper, showing times of goals scored. A blank bar chart is available on page 45. Discuss the need for grouping data when there are many different values. Show how, if each minute had a separate column on a bar chart, the chart would be too large! Different children could work on different sets of data and compare findings.

**Developing Numeracy
Handling Data Year 6
© A & C Black 2002**

Sports day

In a school welly-tossing competition, the field is marked in metre sections, like this:

Throw from here	1 point	2 points	3 points	4 points	5 points	6 points	7 points	8 points	9 points	10 points	11 points

Pupils toss the welly and score points for the section it lands in. They score <u>nothing</u> if they step over the line as they throw. This bar chart shows the results.

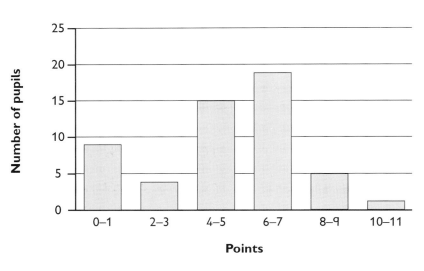

1. How many: **(a)** scored 0 or 1? _____ **(b)** scored 4 or 5? _____

  (c) scored 6 or 7? _____ **(d)** scored 8 or 9? _____

2. Did more than half of the pupils score more than 5 points? _____

3. Did 15 pupils score exactly 5 points? Explain your answer.

_____

4. Why do you think more pupils scored 0 or 1 point than scored 2 or

  3 points? _____

5. If no children scored exactly 10 points, how many points did the winner

  score? _____

• How many children took part in the competition? _____

Teachers' note Use this sheet to explore grouped data shown on a bar chart. Encourage the children to discuss the possible scores of the children in one group by asking: *Is it possible that no one scored 4 points? Is it possible that 9 children scored 0 points?* The children could try this competition for themselves and draw frequency tables and bar charts to show their data.

**Developing Numeracy
Handling Data Year 6
© A & C Black 2002**

A stone's throw

Matt and Li threw two stones into the sea. The │line graph│ shows the heights of the stones from the moment they were thrown.

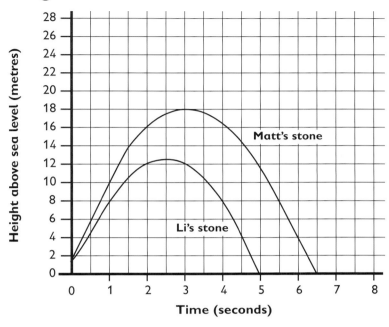

1. At about what height was Li's stone at: **(a)** 1 second? _____

   (b) 3 seconds? _____ **(c)** 4 seconds? _____ **(d)** 5 seconds? _____

2. At about what height was Matt's stone at: **(a)** 1 second? _____

   (b) $1\frac{1}{2}$ seconds? _____ **(c)** 5 seconds? _____ **(d)** $5\frac{1}{2}$ seconds? _____

3. At about how many seconds was Matt's stone twice as high as Li's? _____

4. About how many seconds after Li's stone did Matt's fall into the sea? _____

Dad

Both lines are wrong! They do not start at zero.

5. Do you think Dad is correct? Why? _____

_____

_____

Now try this!

Joe is on a cliff 10 metres above Li and Matt.
• Draw a line on the graph to show what his throw might be like.

Explain your line to a partner.

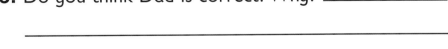

Teachers' note This line graph shows intervals labelled in twos. If necessary, these can be shown in ones (if so, explain that Li and Matt were sitting down when they threw the stones). Encourage the children to discuss and compare their answers to the extension activity. Explain that on any distance–time graph the line never moves back towards the left, as this would imply time moving backwards.

Developing Numeracy
Handling Data Year 6
© A & C Black 2002

Up, up and away

Mum kept some notes of Vikram's height at important times in his life.

At birth he was 50 cm. On his 1st birthday 75 cm.
On his 2nd birthday 88 cm.
He reached 1 metre when he was $3\frac{1}{2}$ years old.
On his 5th birthday 110 cm. He grew only
2 cm between his 5th and 6th birthdays.
Between age 6 and age 11 he grew about the
same each year.
On his 11th birthday 137 cm.

- **Draw a line graph to show Vikram's height from birth to the age of 11.**
- **Use your graph to help you answer the questions.**

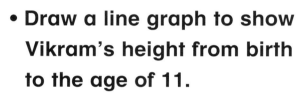

Age (years)

1. Write Vikram's approximate height on these birthdays:

   (a) 3rd _____   **(b)** 4th _____   **(c)** 7th _____

   (d) 8th _____   **(e)** 9th _____   **(f)** 10th _____

2. About how old was Vikram when he was 80 cm tall? _____

3. How many centimetres did he grow in his first two years? _____

4. For about how many years was he between 100 cm and 110 cm? _____

5. About how tall was he aged $7\frac{1}{2}$? _____

- **Write the difference in Vikram's height each year.**

Age	Height	Difference
Birth	50 cm	—
1	75 cm	25 cm

Teachers' note Remind the children to plot all the points on the graph and then join them using a ruler. Ensure the children realise that their answers to the questions are only approximations or estimates. A blank line graph is available on page 46.

**Developing Numeracy
Handling Data Year 6
© A & C Black 2002**

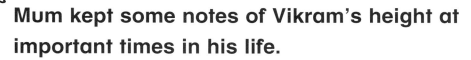

Mum kept some notes of Vikram's height at important times in his life.

At birth he was 50 cm. On his 1st birthday 75 cm.
On his 2nd birthday 88 cm.
He reached 1 metre when he was $3\frac{1}{2}$ years old.
On his 5th birthday 110 cm. He grew only
2 cm between his 5th and 6th birthdays.
Between age 6 and age 11 he grew about the
same each year.
On his 11th birthday 137 cm.

- **Draw a line graph to show Vikram's height from birth to the age of 11.**
- **Use your graph to help you answer the questions.**

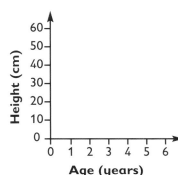
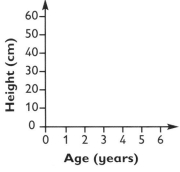

1. About how many centimetres did he grow between

   his 3rd and 4th birthdays? _____

2. **(a)** How many centimetres did he grow in the five years

   between his 6th and 11th birthdays? _____

   (b) How many centimetres is that per year? _____

3. About how tall was he: **(a)** aged 9? _____ **(b)** aged $9\frac{1}{2}$? _____

4. About how old was Vikram when he was 125 cm tall? _____

5. About how many centimetres did he grow in his first 18 months? _____

Now try this!

Here are his twin sister's heights.
- **Plot these on your graph.**
- **At what age were Vikram and Shilpa the same height?** _____
- **How tall were they?** _____

Shilpa's heights	
Birth	45 cm
1st birthday	65 cm
2nd birthday	70 cm
6th birthday	104 cm
8th birthday	130 cm
11th birthday	150 cm

Teachers' note Remind the children to plot all the points on the graph and then join them using a ruler. Ensure the children realise that their answers to the questions are only approximations or estimates. A blank line graph is available on page 46.

**Developing Numeracy
Handling Data Year 6
© A & C Black 2002**

Remember, remember

Ten children did a memory test. On Monday at 7:45 am, they looked carefully at these ten symbols, in this order.

During the week, they did tests to see how well they could remember the symbols in the correct order.

Percentage (%) of symbols remembered in order by the ten children

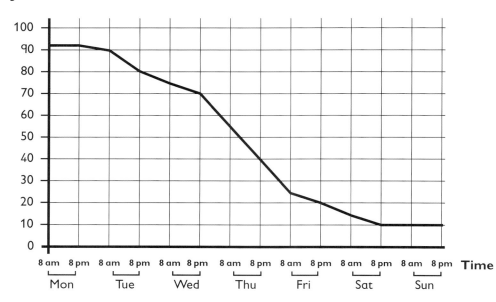

1. What percentage of symbols did the children remember correctly on:

(a) Tuesday at 8 am? _90%_

(b) Friday at 8 pm? _____

(c) Thursday at 8 pm? _____

(d) Saturday at 8 pm? _____

(e) Wednesday at 8 pm? _____

(f) Tuesday at 8 pm? _____

2. What percentage of symbols did they forget between:

(a) Tuesday at 8 am and Tuesday at 8 pm? _____

(b) Saturday at 8 pm and Sunday at 8 am? _____

3. When was the percentage of symbols remembered:

(a) 75%? _____

(b) 25%? _____

Now try this!

• **During which day was there the biggest drop in the number of symbols remembered?** _____

Teachers' note Discuss that the graph shows all the children's results put together; each of the ten children had to remember ten symbols, making a total of 100 symbols in all, thus each symbol remembered correctly was worth 1%. The children could try this test for themselves and record the results at a given time each day for five days.

Developing Numeracy
Handling Data Year 6
© A & C Black 2002

Remember, remember

Ten children did a memory test. On Monday at 7:45 am, they looked carefully at these ten symbols, in this order.

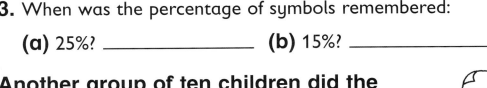

During the week, they did tests to see how well they could remember the symbols in the correct order.

Percentage (%) of symbols remembered in order by the ten children

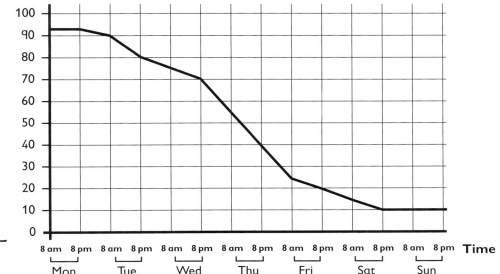

1. What percentage of symbols did the children remember correctly on:

   (a) Tuesday at 8 am? _90%_   **(b)** Wednesday at 8 am? _____

2. What percentage of symbols did they forget between

   Tuesday at 8 am and Tuesday at 8 pm? _____

3. When was the percentage of symbols remembered:

   (a) 25%? _____   **(b)** 15%? _____

Another group of ten children did the memory test, but they could look at the symbols again at noon every day.

4. Look at the results. Plot them on the graph above.

	8 am	8 pm
Monday	92%	95%
Tuesday	91%	93%
Wednesday	88%	90%
Thursday	82%	85%
Friday	78%	84%
Saturday	78%	85%
Sunday	80%	86%

Now try this!

• **Write five differences between the two lines.**

Teachers' note Discuss that the graph shows all the children's results put together; each of the ten children had to remember ten symbols, making a total of 100 symbols in all, thus each symbol remembered correctly was worth 1%. Encourage the children to suggest reasons for the differences between the two lines. They could try the test for themselves over a five-day period.

Developing Numeracy
Handling Data Year 6
© A & C Black 2002

Pop star

TV viewers vote for their favourite contestant.

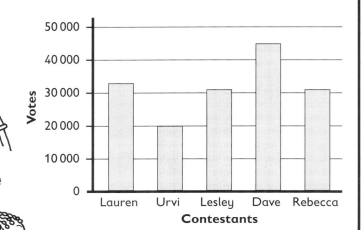

This bar chart shows the number of votes for each contestant by 7 pm.

Between 7 pm and 8 pm more people voted.

This line graph shows the number of votes for one of the contestants, in ten-minute intervals in the last hour.

1. Which contestant's votes does this line graph show? _____

2. If the voting stopped at 8 pm, how many votes did this contestant get in total? _____

....**Voting update**....
During the last hour, Rebecca got an extra 27 000 votes, but Dave got no votes at all.
At 8 pm Lauren had a **total** of 57 000 votes.

3. Who had more votes in total at 8 pm:

(a) Lauren or Dave? _____   **(b)** Rebecca or Lauren? _____

This table shows how many votes Lesley had, in ten-minute intervals between 7 pm and 8 pm.

7:10	33 000
7:20	40 000
7:30	44 000
7:40	49 000
7:50	56 000
8:00	59 000

4. Draw a line graph to show this.

Now try this!
• **Who had the most votes in total at 8 pm?** _____

Teachers' note Encourage discussion about who made the most and least improvement during the last hour. The children could show the final number of votes for all the contestants at 8 pm on a bar chart (using the blank chart on page 45). Ask questions such as: *If the contestant with fewest votes is eliminated, who will be eliminated this week? Who is likely to be eliminated next week?*

**Developing Numeracy
Handling Data Year 6
© A & C Black 2002**

Clever conversions

Conversion graphs help you to convert from one measure to another.

- **Use this** conversion graph **to compare centimetres and inches.**

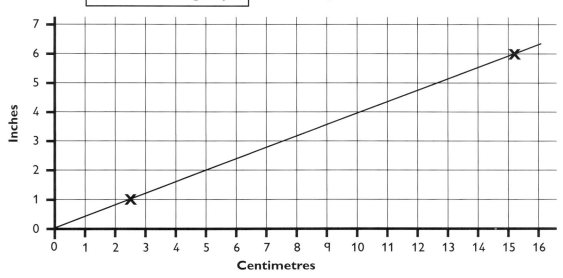

Centimetres

1. About how many **centimetres** is:

(a) 1 inch? _____

(b) 2 inches? _____

(c) $1\frac{1}{2}$ inches? _____

(d) 5·5 inches? _____

(e) $3\frac{1}{2}$ inches? _____

(f) 4 inches? _____

(g) 4·3 inches? _____

Be as accurate as you can.

2. About how many **inches** is:

(a) 4 cm? _____

(b) 5 cm? _____

(c) 14 cm? _____

(d) 6·5 cm? _____

(e) 11 cm? _____

(f) 12 cm? _____

(g) 7 cm? _____

Now try this!

- **Draw your own conversion graph for grams and ounces.**

Label the vertical axis (ounces) in ones, and the horizontal axis (grams) in 25s.

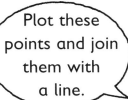

Plot these points and join them with a line.

```
0 ounces = 0 grams
7 ounces ≈ 200 grams
10·5 ounces ≈ 300 grams
```

Your teacher will give you a recipe in ounces .

- **Use your graph to convert it to** grams .

Teachers' note Demonstrate how to convert measurements using a conversion graph, and revise metric and imperial units. Remind the children that these are approximate values only. For the extension activity, give the children a simple recipe in ounces. Once they have completed the activity, they could write pairs of approximately equivalent measurements, for example 2 ounces ≈ 56 grams.

Developing Numeracy
Handling Data Year 6
© A & C Black 2002

Tantalising tables

- **Follow these instructions. They will help you draw a line graph to check your times tables.**

What to do

☆ Write the numbers 0 to 10 along the horizontal axis. Label this **The number to multiply by □**. Choose a times table. Write the number in the box.

☆ Write numbers going up in 5s on the vertical axis. Label this **Answer**.

☆ Now write three facts you know from your chosen times table.

☆ Mark these on your graph. Join the points with a ruler to make a straight line. Your line <u>must</u> go through (0, 0).

Now you can use your graph to find any facts in the times table. You can even find approximate answers for multiplying your chosen number by fractions or decimals, like $5\frac{1}{2}$ or 0·5.

- **Find as many multiplication facts as you can, using the line on your graph.**

  List them on the back of this sheet.

Now try this!

- **On the <u>same</u> graph, draw lines for two other times tables.**

  Label each line.

- **Which line is:** the steepest? _____

  the least steep? _____

- **Write what you notice about how steep the lines are.**

  _____

Teachers' note Show the children an example graph and demonstrate how to read answers by starting from the number to be multiplied by on the horizontal axis, moving up until the line is reached and then reading across from this point to find the answer on the vertical axis. Remind the children that for fractions and decimals the answers are approximate values only.

Developing Numeracy Handling Data Year 6 © A & C Black 2002

Bath-time

Six people had baths between 7 pm and 8 pm. The line graphs show the water level in each bath during this hour.

a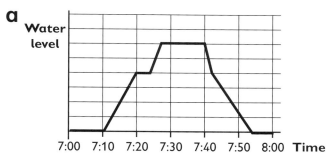

b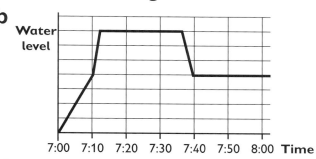

c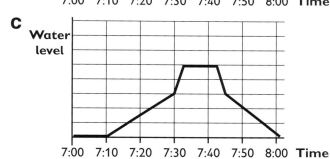

d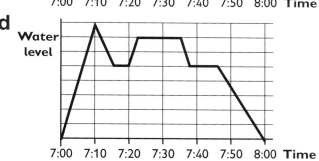

e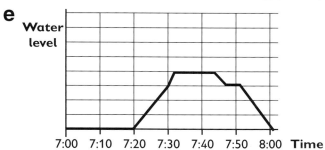

f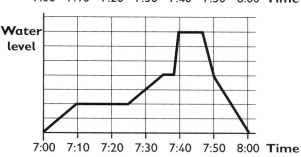

• Match each graph to the correct person.

1. Ahmed overfilled his bath. He had to let some water out before he got in. ☐ d

2. Janet started running her bath at 7:00. The phone rang at 7:10 so she turned off the taps. She started running it again at 7:25. ☐

3. Emma got into the bath at 7:30. It had taken 20 minutes to fill up. ☐

4. Mr Thomas ran the bath for his young son, Ben. Ben got into the bath at 7:30. ☐

5. Steve forgot to take the plug out after his bath. He only discovered this the next morning! ☐

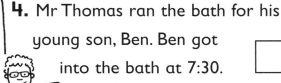 **Now try this!**

• Write a story for the graph that is left.

Teachers' note Encourage the children to discuss the information on the graphs, including when each bath's taps were turned on, when each person got in and when the plug was taken out. They could also look at the amount of water displaced and suggest how large each person is. Discuss that when the line on the graph is steep, it means the bath filled quickly.

**Developing Numeracy
Handling Data Year 6
© A & C Black 2002**

Ploughing patterns

A wall runs along the bottom of a rectangular field. The diagrams show the different ways in which the farmer can plough the field. The graphs show the distance of the tractor from the wall over time.

• Join each diagram to its matching graph.

1.
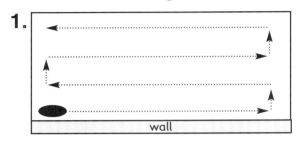

a Distance from wall
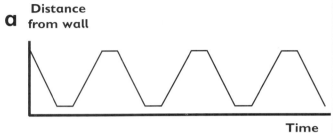
Time

2.
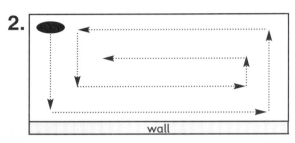

b Distance from wall
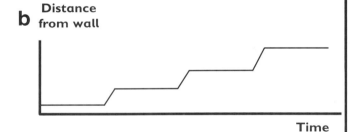
Time

3.
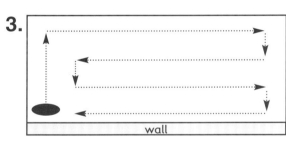

c Distance from wall
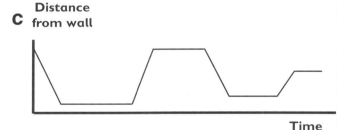
Time

4.
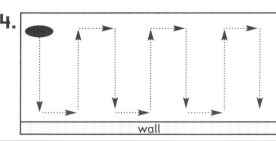

d Distance from wall
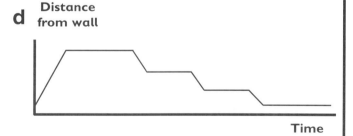
Time

• Draw a line graph for this diagram.
• Now draw your own diagram and line graph.

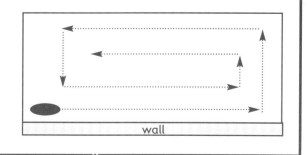

Teachers' note The children may find it useful to mark points on the ploughing diagrams, such as the furthest/closest distances from/to the wall. In the extension activity, remind the children that the line of the graph will always move to the right as time moves forwards. Explain that on any distance–time graph the line never moves back towards the left, as this would imply time moving backwards.

**Developing Numeracy
Handling Data Year 6
© A & C Black 2002**

Crisp pie?

- **Choose 12 people in your class to take part in a survey.**
- **Record which of these crisp flavours they prefer.**

Flavour of crisp	Tally	Frequency
Cheese and onion		
Prawn cocktail		
Ready salted		
Salt and vinegar		
Smoky bacon		

- **Colour each twelfth of the** pie chart **to show the number of votes for each flavour.**

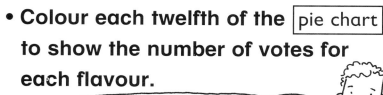

Show segments for the same flavour side-by-side.

- **Write a title. Then write a key to show which flavour each colour represents.**

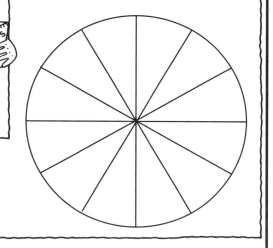

Key ☐ ☐ ☐ ☐ ☐

1. What fraction of the people voted for: **(a)** Cheese and onion? ____

   (b) Prawn cocktail? ____   **(c)** Ready salted? ____

   (d) Salt and vinegar? ____   **(e)** Smoky bacon? ____

2. Which flavour(s) were:

   (a) the most popular? _____

   (b) the least popular? _____

Now try this!

- **Choose a new topic. Survey 12 people.**
- **Draw a pie chart of the new information.**

Teachers' note By using each segment of the pie chart to represent one person in the survey, the children can appreciate the link between this pie chart and charts such as bar charts. For the extension, provide children with copies of the first blank pie chart on page 44. Some children could survey 24 people and use the second pie chart on page 44.

Developing Numeracy
Handling Data Year 6
© A & C Black 2002

Happy holidays

A class surveyed 24 children who went on holiday.

• Look at the pie chart. It shows the type of accommodation each child stayed in.

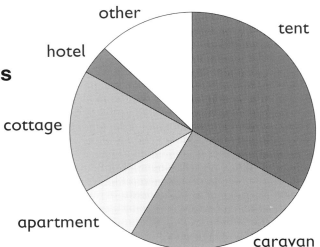

1. Which was the most common type of accommodation? _____

2. What fraction of the children stayed in:

   (a) a caravan? _____ (b) a cottage or an apartment? _____

   (c) a caravan, cottage or an apartment? _____

   (d) a tent? _____ (e) a caravan or apartment? _____

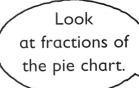

• Imagine the pie split into ⟨24⟩ equal slices. Each slice shows one child's accommodation. Mark these slices on the pie.

3. What fraction of the children stayed in:

   (a) a hotel? _____ (b) a cottage? _____

   (c) an apartment? _____ (d) another type ('other')? _____

4. How many children stayed in:

   (a) a caravan? _____ (b) a hotel? _____

   (c) a cottage? _____ (d) a tent? _____

   (e) an apartment? _____ (f) another type ('other')? _____

• If two of the children stayed at their grandma's house, how many children could have stayed on a boat? _____

Teachers' note Show the children how to split the pie into 24 equal slices by first splitting it into quarters. These quarters can then be split in half to make eight slices, and each of these can be split into three smaller slices the size of the 'hotel' section. The page could be simplified by masking the 'hotel' section (making it part of the 'other' section), and changing the number of children to 12.

Developing Numeracy
Handling Data Year 6
© A & C Black 2002

Molly's mix

Molly mixes together different drinks to make a special party mix.

- **Look at the pie chart. It shows the proportions of the different drinks she uses.**

- **Colour the segments of the pie chart.**

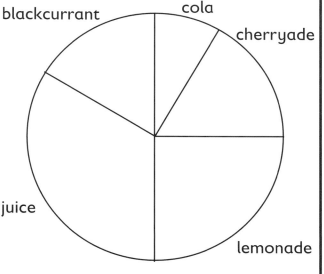

blackcurrant   cola   cherryade

orange juice

lemonade

1. What fraction of the mix is: **(a)** lemonade?  $\frac{1}{4}$

   (b) orange juice? _____   **(c)** cola? _____

   (d) blackcurrant? _____   **(e)** cherryade? _____

Look at fractions of the pie chart.

2. If Molly makes 12 litres of the mix, how many litres of it is: **(a)** lemonade? _____ l

   (b) orange juice? _____ l   **(c)** cola? _____ l

   (d) blackcurrant? _____ l   **(e)** cherryade? _____ l

3. If Molly makes 6 litres of the mix, how many litres of it is: **(a)** lemonade? _____ l

   (b) orange juice? _____ l   **(c)** cola? _____ l

   (d) blackcurrant? _____ l   **(e)** cherryade? _____ l

4. If Molly makes 240 ml of the mix, how many millilitres of it is: **(a)** lemonade? _____ ml

   (b) orange juice? _____ ml   **(c)** cola? _____ ml

   (d) blackcurrant? _____ ml   **(e)** cherryade? _____ ml

Now try this!

- **Make up a recipe for _your_ special party mix. Draw a pie chart to show the proportions of ingredients.**

Teachers' note This activity involves pie charts where the whole is an amount of liquid rather than the number of people surveyed. You could ask the children more questions about amounts of ingredients for different amounts of the 'mix'. For the extension, provide copies of the first blank pie chart on page 44. Some children could use the second pie chart on page 44.

Developing Numeracy Handling Data Year 6 © A & C Black 2002

• **Look at the pie charts for different countries around the world. The charts show the proportions of the population that belong to different religions.**

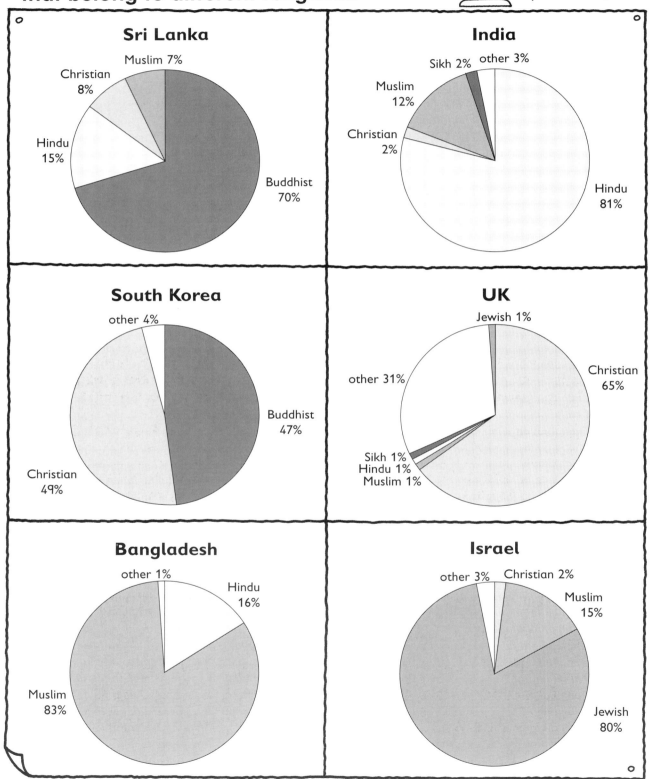

Sri Lanka

Muslim 7%
Christian 8%
Hindu 15%
Buddhist 70%

India

Sikh 2%
other 3%
Muslim 12%
Christian 2%
Hindu 81%

South Korea

other 4%
Buddhist 47%
Christian 49%

UK

Jewish 1%
other 31%
Christian 65%
Sikh 1%
Hindu 1%
Muslim 1%

Bangladesh

other 1%
Hindu 16%
Muslim 83%

Israel

other 3%
Christian 2%
Muslim 15%
Jewish 80%

Teachers' note Use this with page 39. Show the children a world map and identify the locations of the countries. Discuss the different religions and explain that 'other' can include many different religions or those who do not follow a religion of any kind. Ask the children to think about whether the pie charts give any information about the *number* of people with a particular religion.

**Developing Numeracy
Handling Data Year 6
© A & C Black 2002**

Which religion? 2

• **Look carefully at the sheet called Which religion? 1.**

1. What religion are most people in:

    (a) Sri Lanka? <u>Buddhist</u>   **(b)** India? _____

    (c) South Korea? _____   **(d)** the UK? _____

    (e) Bangladesh? _____   **(f)** Israel? _____

2. What percentage of the population is Muslim in:

    (a) South Korea? <u>Less than 4%</u>   **(b)** India? _____

    (c) Sri Lanka? _____   **(d)** Bangladesh? _____

    (e) Israel? _____   **(f)** the UK? _____

3. Write the correct country for each statement.

(a)
It has approximately the same number of Christians as Buddhists.

(b)
Just over three quarters of the population is Jewish.

(c)
About two thirds of the population is Christian.

(d)
Just over three quarters of the population is Hindu.

(e)
There are about the same number of Muslims as Sikhs.

(f)
About one sixth of the population is Muslim.

Now try this!

• **In which two countries is the second religion:**

    Hinduism? _____ and _____

    Islam? _____ and _____

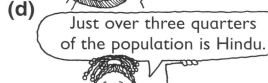
Islam is the Muslim religion.

• **Can these pie charts tell us whether there are more Buddhists in the countries than Hindus? Why/why not?**

_____

Teachers' note Use this with page 38. As a further extension, the children could sketch a simple pie chart using the information for the Czech Republic: 47% Christian, 40% atheist, 13% other. Further information about world religions can be found in 'The World Factbook' on the website www.bartleby.com

**Developing Numeracy
Handling Data Year 6
© A & C Black 2002**

People in our group

- **Your group is going to plan a survey.**
- **Fill in the boxes below. You must all agree.**

Favourite computer game?

What we plan to survey (think carefully about what you are hoping to find out, and whether people will want to tell you that information)

What resources we will need

What we think the results of the survey are likely to be

- **Now you are going to write a recording sheet for your survey. You could also write a questionnaire.**

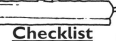
Checklist ✓

Think carefully about your questions.
- Could people misunderstand them?
- What are the possible answers?
- Do you need to suggest possible answers for people to choose from?

Think carefully about your recording sheet.
- Is there enough space to record the information?
- How quick will it be to fill in? Can you make it quicker?
- Can you allow extra space for writing any interesting comments?

Teachers' note Use this with pages 41 and 42. Discuss this planning sheet with the class before organising the children into groups. Ensure that the children understand what is required, and suggest different ways in which they could work, distribute responsibility within the group, and record and present the information. Discuss the differences between a recording sheet and a questionnaire.

Developing Numeracy Handling Data Year 6 © A & C Black 2002

Data project: questionnaires

Here are two questionnaires.
One is much better than the other.
• **Can you see why?**

Do you watch TV?
How often do you watch it?
For how long do you watch it?
What is your favourite type of programme?
What is your favourite programme?

1. Do you watch TV?   yes   no
   (If no, stop the survey now)   ☐   ☐

2. How often do you watch TV?   every day   ☐
                                      most days   ☐
                                      once or twice a week   ☐
                                      less than once a week ☐
                                      other _____

3. For about how many hours a week do you watch TV?
   more than 28 hours (more than 4 hours a day)   ☐
   between 14 and 28 hours (about 2–4 hours a day)   ☐
   between 7 and 14 hours (about 1–2 hours a day)   ☐
   less than 7 hours (less than 1 hour a day)   ☐
   other _____

4. What are your favourite types of programme?
   comedies   ☐   soaps   ☐
   news   ☐   documentaries   ☐
   reality TV   ☐   wildlife/nature   ☐
   films   ☐   children's   ☐
   cartoons   ☐   dramas   ☐
   other _____

5. What is your favourite programme? _____

• **Give reasons why the second questionnaire is better.**

• **Find ways to improve the second questionnaire.**

Teachers' note This sheet can be used with pages 40 and 42 to help with the children's data project. Discuss the features of the second questionnaire, such as the sentence following question 1, and draw attention to numbering, tick boxes, wording of questions, and so on. Discuss improvements that could still be made. The children could write further questions for this survey and carry it out.

**Developing Numeracy
Handling Data Year 6**
© A & C Black 2002

Data project: interpreting

- **Imagine you are reporting the results of your survey in a newspaper.**

1. Write an explanation of the purpose of your survey, what you did and how you carried it out.

_____

_____

_____

_____

2. Now write about your findings. Use some of these words and phrases to write statements about the information you gathered.

most popular
most common
favourite
mode
least popular
least common

same number as
half as many as
twice as many
large difference
small difference
range

_____

_____

_____

_____

3. Did the results of your survey turn out the way you expected?   yes ☐   no ☐

4. What was the most unexpected part of the survey?

_____

5. If you were to do this survey again, what would you change?

_____

_____

Teachers' note This sheet can be used with pages 40 and 41 or following any survey that the children have carried out. The children could also present their findings in other ways, for example, as a script for a television documentary or as an interview in which one child plays the role of the interviewer and asks appropriate questions.

**Developing Numeracy
Handling Data Year 6
© A & C Black 2002**

Blank probability scales

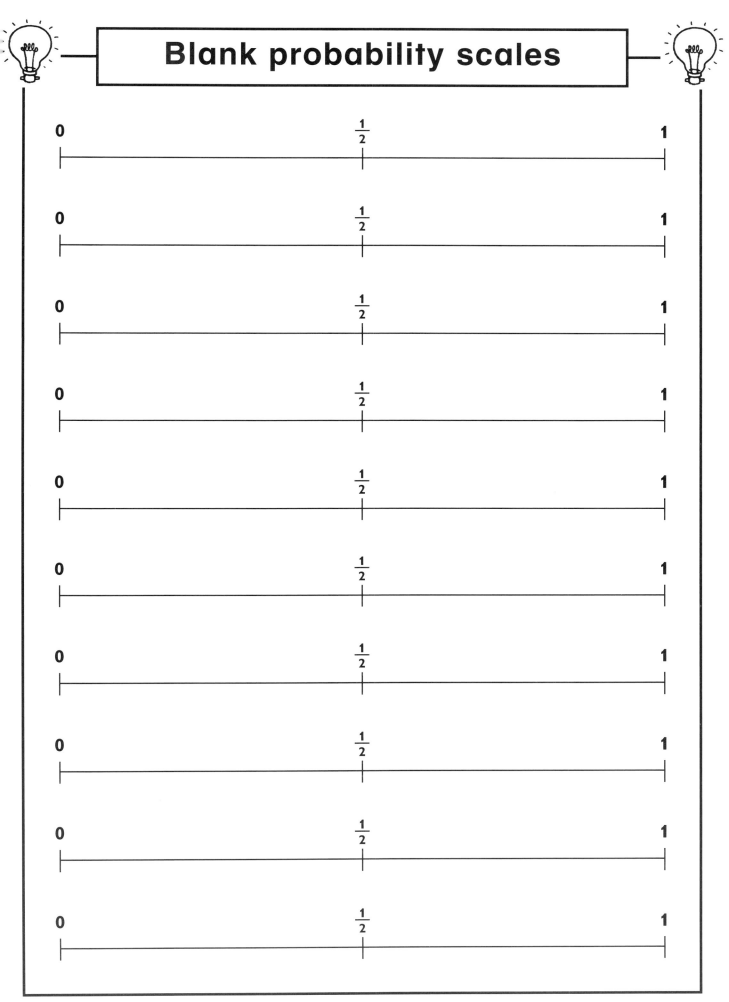

Teachers' note This sheet provides a flexible resource. It can be enlarged on a photocopier. Mark the lines in fifths or sixths before copying if necessary.

Developing Numeracy
Handling Data Year 6
© A & C Black 2002

Blank pie charts

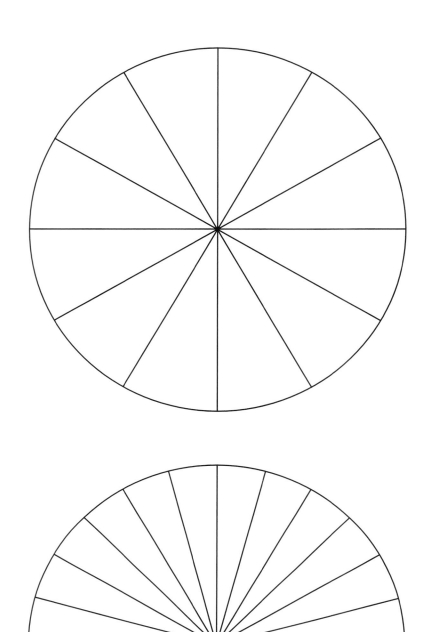

Teachers' note This sheet provides a flexible resource. It can be enlarged on a photocopier. Remind the children of the importance of giving their chart a title.

Developing Numeracy
Handling Data Year 6
© A & C Black 2002

Blank bar chart

A bar chart to show _____

_____

Teachers' note This sheet provides a flexible resource. It can be enlarged on a photocopier. Remind the children of the importance of labelling the axes and giving the chart a title.

Developing Numeracy
Handling Data Year 6
© A & C Black 2002

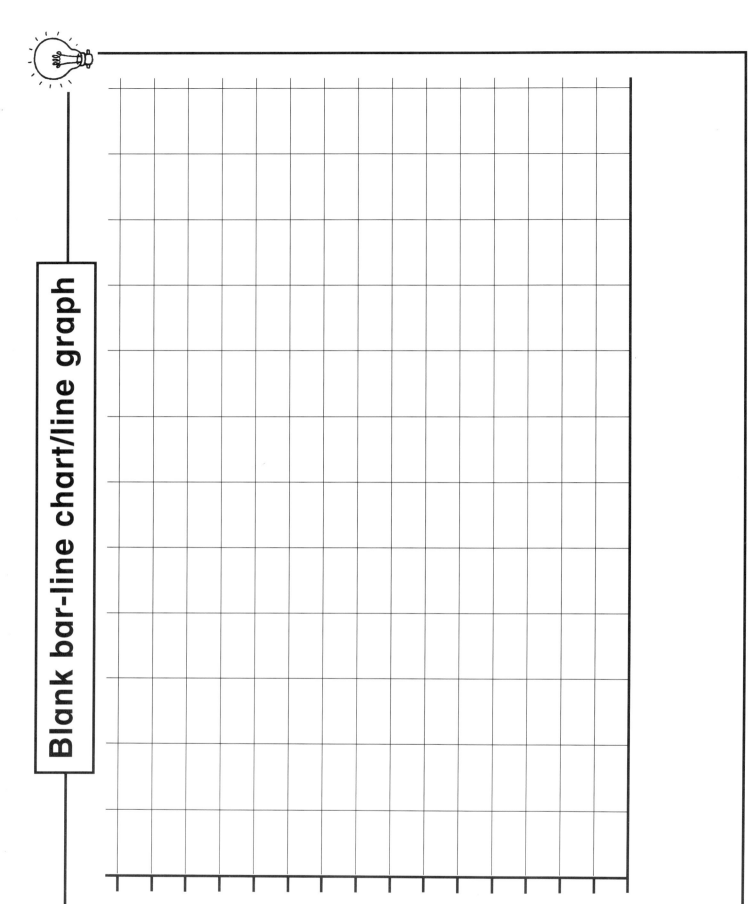

Blank bar-line chart/line graph

Teachers' note This sheet provides a flexible resource. It can be enlarged on a photocopier. Remind the children of the importance of labelling the axes and giving the chart a title.

Developing Numeracy
Handling Data Year 6
© A & C Black 2002

p 6

Now try this!

36 possible outcomes:

2 - 1 + 1					
3 - 1 + 2	2 + 1				
4 - 1 + 3	3 + 1	2 + 2			
5 - 1 + 4	4 + 1	2 + 3	3 + 2		
6 - 1 + 5	5 + 1	2 + 4	4 + 2	3 + 3	
7 - 1 + 6	6 + 1	2 + 5	5 + 2	3 + 4	4 + 3
8 - 2 + 6	6 + 2	3 + 5	5 + 3	4 + 4	
9 - 3 + 6	6 + 3	4 + 5	5 + 4		
10 - 4 + 6	6 + 4	5 + 5			
11 - 5 + 6	6 + 5				
12 - 6 + 6					

p 9

1. $1/10$ 2. $2/10$ or $1/5$
3. $1/10$ 4. $4/10$ or $2/5$
5. $1/10$ 6. 0
7. $3/10$ 8. $7/10$
9. $9/10$
10. $9/10$
11. $6/10$ or $2/10$
12. $3/10$
13. $10/10$ or 1

Now try this!

p 10

1. Fatima $1/8$ and Jack 0
2. Fatima $1/8$ and Jack $1/4$
3. Fatima $2/8$ or $1/4$ and Jack $1/4$
4. Fatima $1/8$ and Jack 0
5. Fatima $3/8$ and Jack $2/4$ or $1/2$

p 12

Situations **a**, **b**, **c**, **d**, **f** and **h** should be ticked.

p 15

1. (a) mistle thrush
   (b) goldcrest
   (c) blackbird
   (d) goldcrest
2. (a) 21 cm   (b) 10 cm
3. (a) 8 g   (b) 99 g
4. (a) blue tit and treecreeper
   (b) 11 g and 9 g
5. (a) swallow and starling
   (b) 18 g and 69 g
6. (a) robin and great tit
   (b) 14 cm and 14 cm

p 16

1. Chandu
2. Mabel
3. Dorothy
4. Danny
5. (a) 95   (b) 73
6. (a) Kylie and Sam   (b) 113 and 70
7. (a) Alfred and Jennie   (b) 66 and 36
8. (a) 88   (b) 80
9. Yes (5 out of 8)
10. No (0 out of 3)

Now try this!

In order of age	In order of scores
Chandu 6	Danny 37
Danny 7	David 42
David 8	Nagajan 45
Lauren 9	Chandu 54
Rebecca and Nagajan 11	Mabel 67
Chloe 15	Lauren 69
Deepa 18	Gordon and Sam 70
Sam and Kylie 24	Franco 73
Lesley 34	Chloe 84
Jennie 36	Jennifer and Alfred 87
Franco 38	Edith 89
Jeremy 40	Lesley 93
Vincento 45	Deepa 95

Gordon 49	Vincento 99
Dorothy 54	Rebecca 100
Alfred 66	Jeremy 101
Edith 84	Kylie 113
Mabel 94	Dorothy 117

p 17

1. (a) 9
   (b) 7
   (c) 7
   (d) 6
2. (a) 9
   (b) 1 (or A)
   (c) 4
   (d) 5
3. (a) 5
   (b) 6
   (c) 5
   (d) 4
4. (a) 7
   (b) 8
   (c) 6
   (d) 6
5. (a) 8
   (b) 9
   (c) 4
   (d) 5
6. (a) 7
   (b) 6 and 9
   (c) 6
   (d) 6

p 19

1. 4
2. 8
3. A number above 4
4. 3
5. 5
6. 7
7. 7 and two numbers above 7
8. 4, 6, 8

Now try this!

6, 0 and 6

p 20

1. (a) 1   (b) 3
   (c) 4   (d) 78
2. (a) 1   (b) 0
   (c) 1   (d) 74
3. (a) 1958 and 1967   (b) 1948 and 1957
   (c) 1978 and 1987   (d) 1928 and 1937
4. The introduction of Satellite and Cable TV
5. Mode 1 and 3, mean 11·5
As the range is so large these averages are less useful than with a smaller range.

Now try this!

Check children's answers are reasonable.

p 24

1. (a) 9   (b) 15
   (c) 19   (d) 5
2. No
3. Possible, but only if no one scored 4.
4. Some may have stepped over the line when throwing.
5. 11

Now try this!

53

p 25

1. (a) 8 m
   (b) 12 m   (c) 8 m   (d) 0 m
2. (a) 10 m
   (b) 14 m   (c) 12 m   (d) 8 m
3. 4
4. 1 $1/2$
5. No, because stone is thrown from arm level, not ground level.

p 26
1. (a) Between 94 cm and 97 cm
   (b) Between 102 cm and 105 cm
   (c) 117 cm
   (d) 122 cm
   (e) 127 cm
   (f) 132 cm
2. About 1
3. 38 cm
4. $1\frac{1}{2}$
5. About 120 cm

p 27
1. Between 5 cm and 10 cm
2. (a) 25 cm   **(b)** 5 cm
3. (a) 127 cm   **(b)** Between 127 cm and 130 cm
4. About 8
5. About 32 cm
Now try this!
Age 7
117 cm tall

p 28
1. (a) 90%   **(b)** 20%
   (c) 40%   **(d)** 10%
   (e) 70%   **(f)** 80%
2. (a) 10%
   (b) 0%
3. (a) Wednesday 8 am
   (b) Friday 8 am
Now try this!
Thursday

p 29
1. (a) 90%   **(b)** 75%
2. 10%
3. (a) Friday 8 am   **(b)** Saturday 8 am
4. Check children have plotted results correctly.

p 30
1. Urvi
2. 35 000
3. Lauren
4. Rebecca
Now try this!
Lesley

p 31
1. (a) About 2·5 cm
   (b) Just under 5 cm
   (c) Just under 4 cm
   (d) About 14 cm
   (e) About 9 cm
   (f) About 10 cm
   (g) About 11 cm
2. (a) About 1·5 inches
   (b) About 2 inches
   (c) About 5·5 inches
   (d) About 2·5 inches
   (e) About 4·3 inches
   (f) About 4·7 inches
   (g) About 2·8 inches

p 33
1. d   **2.** f   **3.** c   **4.** e   **5.** b

p 34
1. b   **2.** c   **3.** d   **4.** a

p 36
1. Tent
2. (a) $\frac{1}{4}$ **(b)** $\frac{1}{4}$
   (c) $\frac{1}{2}$
   (d) $\frac{8}{24}$ or $\frac{1}{3}$ **(e)** $\frac{8}{24}$ or $\frac{1}{3}$
3. (a) $\frac{1}{24}$ **(b)** $\frac{4}{24}$ or $\frac{1}{6}$
   (c) $\frac{2}{24}$ or $\frac{1}{12}$ **(d)** $\frac{3}{24}$ or $\frac{1}{8}$
4. (a) 6   **(b)** 1
   (c) 4   **(d)** 8
   (e) 2   **(f)** 3
Now try this!
i

p 37
1. (a) $\frac{1}{4}$
   (b) $\frac{1}{3}$ **(c)** $\frac{1}{12}$
   (d) $\frac{1}{6}$ **(e)** $\frac{1}{6}$
2. (a) 3 l
   (b) 4 l   **(c)** 1 l
   (d) 2 l   **(e)** 2 l
3. (a) 1·5 l
   (b) 2 l   **(c)** 0·5 l
   (d) 1 l   **(e)** 1 l
4. (a) 60 ml
   (b) 80 ml   **(c)** 20 ml
   (d) 40 ml   **(e)** 40 ml

p 39
1. (a) Buddhist   **(b)** Hindu
   (c) Christian   **(d)** Christian
   (e) Muslim   **(f)** Jewish
2. (a) Less than 4%   **(b)** 12%
   (c) 7%   **(d)** 83%
   (e) 15%   **(f)** 1%
3. (a) South Korea   **(b)** Israel
   (c) UK   **(d)** India
   (e) UK   **(f)** Israel
Now try this!
Hinduism: Sri Lanka and Bangladesh
Islam: India and Israel
Not always, because Buddhism and Hinduism sometimes fall into
'Other' category.